BEAU PEEP

Colour Collection

from THE STAR

£2.95

Printed by Eyre & Spottiswoode, Cosham, Hants.; Reproduction by Graphic Origination, & co-ordinated by Roeder Print Services Ltd.

BEAU PEEP

EGON

THE NOMAD

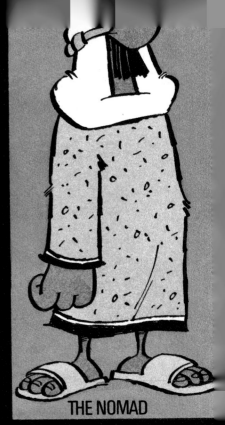

MAD PIERRE

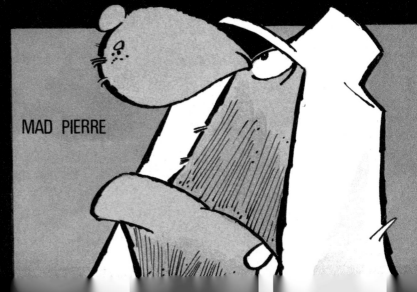

DENNIS

HAMISH

SERGEANT BIDET

COLONEL ESCARGOT

THE VULTURE

Welcome to Beau Peep's latest creation and let me say on his behalf: enjoy yourself!

In fact, co-authors Roger Kettle and Andrew Christine have produced this collectors item to make sure that we all have a good laugh, enjoy the special wit and charm of Beau & Co.

The world's too serious a place these days – we need the antics of Beau and his desert chums to brighten all our lives.

As you flick through this book – and then study it in detail – I am sure you will agree that this is exactly what Andrew and Roger have achieved.

I get great pleasure in turning to the back page of The Star every day to read Beau Peep. In my privileged position as Editor I could sneak a look to preview days, even weeks, in advance. But I don't.

It would spoil my morning. Whatever the news, however serious the affairs of the day, that strip across the bottom of The Star cheers me instantly.

I know this publication will do the same for you. We now have a fun award at The Star called the Dennis Pratt Award, named after another Beau character.

It is granted for "outstanding stupidity". The award that should be given for this publication is for "outstanding originality". Enjoy it! I am.

Best wishes.

Lloyd Turner
EDITOR

THE ADVENTURES OF LEGIONNAIRE
BEAU PEEP

FROM **THE STAR**

WHAT ARE YOU DOING DENNIS?

I'M GOING TO MAKE A SHIP IN A BOTTLE.

THAT'S REALLY DIFFICULT DO YOU KNOW THE SECRET?

SECRET? WHAT SECRET?

YOU MAKE A SHIP AND YOU BUNG IT IN A BOTTLE!

BUT, DENNIS, IT'S—

DON'T TELL *ME* HOW TO PUT A SHIP IN A BOTTLE!

WE'VE MANAGED TO SAVE HIS FINGER BY REMOVING THE GLASS— WE'LL DO THE WOOD SPLINTERS NEXT.

INFIRMARY

A candid shot of writer Roger Kettle on the left and artist Andrew Christine as they try to avoid creditors. In a pathetic attempt to look like pop stars, both are wearing extremely cheap leather jackets – not so much "off the peg" as "off the lorry."

Anyone buying this book will have the undying gratitude of Roger, Andrew, the creditors and the as-yet-unpaid lorry driver.

42

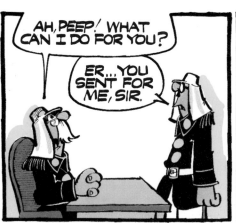

27

33

2

14

13

5

WHAT ARE WE DOING?

ER...NOTHING. EXACTLY!

WHAT SEPARATES US FROM ANIMALS, DENNIS?

ER...

I'LL TELL YOU! THE OLD GREY MATTER! THE ABILITY TO THINK, TO REASON, TO CREATE!

WE'VE GOT TO DO SOMETHING TO USE THIS ABILITY!

D'YOU MEAN LIKE SUMS AND PUZZLES?

WELL, YES, WHY NOT?

12

RIGHT YOU COUNT UP TO FIFTY AND I'LL GO AND HIDE!

7

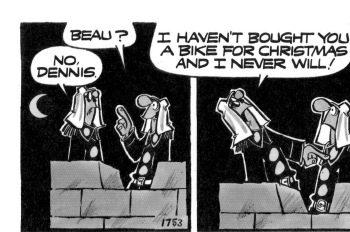

For further adventures of Legionnaire Beau Peep
get

every morning